DATE DUE

N. A.   ME.

GOT TO STOP DRAGGIN'

THAT LITTLE

RED WAGON

AROUND

Books by Robert Paul Smith

So It Doesn't Whistle
The Journey
Because of My Love
The Time and the Place
"Where Did You Go?" "Out." "What Did You
    Do?" "Nothing."
Translations from the English
How to Do Nothing with Nobody All Alone by
    Yourself
How to Grow Up in One Piece
Crank

For Children

Jack Mack
Nothingatall Nothingatall Nothingatall
When I Am Big

Poems

. . . And Another Thing

Play

The Tender Trap (with Max Shulman)

GOT TO STOP DRAGGIN'
THAT LITTLE
RED WAGON
AROUND

by Robert Paul Smith

Harper & Row, Publishers

1817

New York, Evanston, and London

FIRST EDITION

LIBRARY OF CONGRESS CATALOG CARD NUMBER: 69-15264

697071727387654321

To L. J. R.

Everyone, all his life, keeps on draggin' his own particular little red wagon around. Some people have a whole train of them. Some people keep dragging them all, all their lives, some manage to lose a few, some add a few, but all of us keep hauling pieces of our childhood on wheels, usually creaking, behind us.

Most of them are useless, but apparently indispensable. It's a little like England which, in the twentieth century, keeps revealing great jagged chunks of the eighteenth. It is charming, and infuriating. A pair of English shoes are wonderful, precisely because "Sir, we have always done it that way." Putting a phone call through will drive you round the bend for exactly the same reason.

Like the character in Nathanael West's *The Day of the Locust,* life to me is a great succession of exploding stoves. I turn the valve to the same position it was the last time, I put the match to the same place I did last time, and the stove explodes in my face—the same as it did last time. You would think by now I would know that this is not the right way to light a stove, but I will persist in this error, I guess, forever.

What has happened is that, like everyone I know, a piece of childhood is irrevocably stuck in the fabric of my life, there is an extra gear in my drive train, and either I will never again light a stove, or I will go on lighting stoves in such a way that they explode.

I got to thinking about my own little red wagon, loaded to the scuppers with valuable and valueless information, hopelessly mixed. Since the day I was six, and pulled desperately at the post-office door and a ten-foot stranger, bearded and deep-voiced, announced in tones of thunder, "Sonny, the doors of all public buildings open OUT!," I never break for the open without hearing this voice of God. (The information is, alas, dated.) I know, when I mail a letter in an old-fashioned letter box, that it goes down on the first closing clank, but wild horses could not keep me from that extra safety clanking (somebody told me, first time I mailed a letter, that was the way to do it). The world has changed so that a penny postcard costs five cents and a phone call costs a dime, but sending the card will forever in my mental finances cost a penny and be proper, a phone call will cost five times as much and be a self-indulgent extravagance.

A book overdue at the public library will be still something to make hideous the sleepless night. Heaved over the tailgate of my little red wagon is any belief that a horsehair in a rain barrel will turn into a snake, but I will not take bets that a cherry stone swallowed will not bring on instant appendicitis.

I have no hope of emptying or totally untying my wagon. I would like to lighten my load, because so much of it is something I was told when I was six by an eight-year-old who didn't know what the hell he was talking about, having misunderstood what an ignorant and superstitious ten-year-old had told him.

I thought it might be useful to look back at the career of Paul Marrane, a fictional character bearing certain points of identity with myself, in an effort to track down the original circumstance that makes him light stoves in such a way that they go bang. I think that in some cases I have succeeded, but I am sure in others I have only managed to peel one layer off the onion that lives where Paul's brain should be.

I only report that in those instances in which Paul's experience bears an identity with my own, certain bulky items have been jettisoned from my wagon.

I submit that process to you. Lord knows we could all use lighter wagons.

He had been a bug-hunter for some time. Beetles were easy, and the sun turning the carapaces into rainbow metal was a delight. Grasshoppers were easy, but they had started out being sunfish bait, and they never really entered into his world of collecting.

Best of all were butterflies. He made a net of an old piece of broom handle, a wire coat hanger bound on inefficiently and precariously with a quarter mile of doorbell wire and some cheesecloth salvaged from the rag bag on the back of the cellar door. A sister sewed this for him, and made him trickle with embarrassment the whole time. It was a handicap, having a bug-hunter for a brother.

All the kids laughed at him when he went down the street to the woods. It was comic-strip proof of his sissydom.

Hunting was poor.

That summer he was sent away to camp for the first time. It was a camp run by some quasi-religious society devoted to good works and moral values. All the other kids at the camp had attended for years nondenominational prayer meetings of the group, they all knew each other, so he was free most of the time for his own pursuits. The camp had the virtue of regarding children as something better than rough beasts, and it was nice not to be made fun of for being a bug-hunter.

The summer proceeded, and one day he saw a Cecropia moth of unparalleled, unimaginable dimensions. The coat hanger stayed on the broomstick, the cheesecloth bellied out, he turned the handle properly. He owned the biggest, most perfect moth in the history of natural history.

There was a nature study group, and he bore net and moth and himself to the cabin where it was housed. Weeks before, he had built a mounting board, and on a shelf was the communal killing bottle.

The moth was compact of all the colors he loved, burnt browns and oranges, and on the lower wing were two glowing eyespots. From the head sprang the antennae, combs of utter symmetry, made the way a child would draw a feather.

It was hard to bring himself to put the fluttering wonder into the wide-mouthed jar with poison-soaked plaster of Paris at the bottom, but his lust for the impossible perfection of the moth—never in his life would he encounter such a moth again—won out. The moth struggled briefly, and died.

He lifted it out, more gently than he had ever touched anything but himself before, and put it in the relaxing jar, and later on mounted it on the dihedral board, the wings held down by strips of soft paper, the paper held down by tiny pins, a pin thrust, with loathing and love, through the gently furred body.

He ate no candy for two weeks, and paid off the loan of a museum mount, passe partout paper and cotton and isinglass.

It was the best moth in the world.

He took it home at the end of the summer, and was wise enough by that time not to show it to anyone.

He kept it in his top bureau drawer, and looked at it from time to time, only when he was alone, and usually by fading daylight. It was the first satisfactory accomplishment of his life.

And then he forgot about it.

Several months later he remembered, and took it out again and looked at it.

At first he didn't believe what he saw, and then he took it to the window, and looked again, and could not deny the truth of the matter. The lovely wings were ragged at the edges. He looked a little more and saw a tiny beetle feeding on the wings.

He went to the library. There was, it seemed, a special beetle that fed on moths, a continuing problem to museums. Camphor was useful, but not certain.

The moth was nothing, now that it was not perfect. He took it to the place where all imperfections were totally annihilated, where model ships and model planes that would not come right were taken out of his sight.

He opened the door of the coal furnace, and the black box and the isinglass and the moth sat on the red coals for an instant and then became ash.

It took him fifty-two years to find out that it was no

use blaming your mother, your father, your sister, brother, teacher, friend, or foe.

Some things that happened were nobody's fault, there was nothing to blame.

The world itself is unfair.

The sun filtered in through the windows with the dotted-swiss curtains, and the only sound on the sun porch was the creak of the woven wicker chairs. His father sat in one, in his striped shirt sleeves, the starched collar immaculate, the watered-silk tie drawn into a perfect narrow knot, the black pearl stickpin dead center.

His father's eyes, as always, were rimmed with red. He put down the newspaper and removed his pince-nez glasses, and there were two angry little kidney-shaped marks on either side of the bridge of his nose. He put his glasses down on the cane and bamboo table, took his head in both hands, and massaged the kidney-shaped spots, the irritated eyes, the forehead with the vein.

He said nothing. Paul said nothing. There was no one else on the porch. His father sat back in the chair after the knuckling, threw his head back, and closed his eyes.

A fly buzzed on the windowpane. A dog barked. A touring car went down the street.

Paul went back to "The Boys' and Girls' Bookshelf." The pictures were interesting, and he could read a word here and there.

His mother was out shopping.

He was alone in the house with his father. He knew that his father was sick, but in a special way, not the way he or his sister were sometimes sick, and then got well. His father had a sickness that could end only one way. Something would happen, and his father's face would turn black like Mr. Cavery's next door, he would make a strange noise, and fall to the floor like a felled tree, and never get up. It could be anyone's fault, because when his father got angry his face got red. A little more and it would get black and he would fall down and never get up and it would be the fault of whoever made his father angry.

It would not be, Paul had decided, Paul.

There was a noise on the street, kids were coming home from school. After a while, the younger of his two older sisters came in the door right onto the sun porch.

She was smiling, and she was flushed with the heat, and she threw her schoolbooks down on the porch glider, and sat there fanning herself with the bow of her middy blouse. She told her father all about the Latin teacher, and she made him laugh. She got up off the glider and went and sat in her father's lap. They were both laughing, and the wicker chair was creaking. She put her finger on top of her father's head, where the black strands were carefully combed sideways to cover a part of his bald head. She twisted them up into a spike and told her father he looked like Skeezix, like a little baby, and they laughed together.

The glider creaked, and Paul stared unseeing at "The Boys' and Girls' Bookshelf."

He could have done that. He could have if he could have. But he just couldn't. And wouldn't. And never would be able to.

And the rest of his life he would be the patsy of any man in authority who looked at him and smiled.

Eventually, Paul ceased to be a son and, in full time, became a father. They lived in the smelly city and, come summertime, they rented a car and found a house with green grass all around, all around. What had been the clincher was the day Paul sat his fat little boy's bottom on the grass in the park. Two things happened. The kid cried, because he had never felt grass before. The park attendant came by and told Paul kids were not allowed on the grass. Dogs, drunks, pigeons, but not kids.

It was nice in the country. The bed broke, there were hornets under the eaves, with all of the United States at his disposal a blue jay chose the little boy's forehead as a latrine, the beach was far away. Paul's hay fever came back, his wife and son both got prickly heat, and his son alone developed colic.

But in the back yard in the later afternoon, there was a canvas chair for Paul to sit in, a dishpan of water for his son to be dunked in, a fairly cool wife in a tan cotton dress and bare feet, friends to visit once in a while, and (a novelty in those days) a pizza parlor within heat-retaining distance.

Paul was very proud to be a father.

One afternoon he dunked his son in the dishpan under the copper beech tree, sat him on his (Paul's) lap. Paul had turned the hose on himself and he and his son sat there gently dripping. His son on him, he on the chair, the chair on the lawn; and a light breeze came up, they cooled and dried.

"Abba dabba," said Paul.

"Gwarf," said his son.

"Indeed?"

"Gwarf."

"I'll tell him when he comes in."

"Gwarf?"

"You bet your ever-loving . . ."

The conversation proceeded, they were cool and almost dry.

The canvas chair evaporated the damp from Paul's shorts and Paul's shorts evaporated the damp from his bottom.

His son lay against his chest, half asleep, and the blind mouth reached up and closed around Paul's nipple.

It was a strange feeling. Paul detached him immediately.

"Oh, boy, do you have the wrong number!" Paul said.

Paul didn't want to walk to school with his sisters, but when Paul's mother issued marching orders, you either did what she said or were jawed at until you did it and it was easier to say yes in the first place.

Paul's sisters did not want him walking to school with them, either, but in Paul's household the jawing had started early in life, and although they did not say yes, they did not say no, either. The girls had to walk more slowly because of Paul and they did it that way until they were halfway up the hill, but by then his older sister's always short patience always snapped, and she walked her own pace. The not as old sister walked with her, and Paul ran behind, never quite left behind, never quite caught up.

What with the cold weather, the constant sniffle that was part of his legacy turned into a waterfall, and he ran after, with his upper lip glistening and starting to smart in the chill.

His older sister turned round and saw him. She put

her hands on her hips and regarded him with the ordinary loathing of an older sister for a kid brother. Also, Paul and this sister did not like each other at all, just as people, let alone as siblings.

As he came up to her, she stuck out her hand. "The one for blow, you terrible little snot," she said.

Paul reached in his pocket for one of the two handkerchiefs the schoolkids of that generation had always with them. One clean to show the teacher (one to show), and one indifferently clean to mop with (one to blow).

He handed it to her and stuck out his face.

She took his nose in the folded handkerchief and said, "Blow, you terrible little snot," and he did and then she wiped and it seemed to Paul she was pulling his nose out by the roots.

They looked at each other. He could not prove she had squeezed harder than absolutely necessary, and she knew it, but that didn't mean that when they got back home he wouldn't complain of her to their mother.

"Oh, come on, we'll be late," said the older sister, and they proceeded to walk through the vale of sunshine and birdcalls, childhood, the two of them not far enough ahead of him so that he lost sight, nor near enough to be with. His nose was running again. He thought it might be a good time to cry.

When Paul first came to work at the square office, he found himself as much out of tempo as he always did in an office, but worse. As the years had gone by, offices seemed to have reached a point where—as the affluent society afflued—less and less work was being done in more and more time by fewer and fewer people. He adjured himself to watch it, and take it easy, and write what was required and put it in his desk drawer and leave it there for a couple of weeks so that they would figure he'd spent a lot of time on it.

He kept telling himself and telling himself to do this, but as always a loud voice screamed in his ear, "Shit or get off the pot!" and he found himself saying, "What you ought to do"—and here sometimes he remembered to put in the phrase "in my opinion"—"is so and so." As time wore on his patience grew less, and he said, "Give me a pencil and a piece of paper," and in front of the real square johns, he scribbled what he thought—hell, what he *knew*—was the pitiful solution of the pitiful problem.

The square johns, of course, jibbed at this, thinking Paul was going fast to make them look slow, but after a while they found out that his answers were—more often than not—the correct answers, and after a while he found a square john with somewhat abraded corners who not only accepted the answers but was enthusiastic about them. The word spread, and Paul became the guy in the office you went to when your ass was in a sling and you needed an answer in a hurry.

The other thing that happened was that Paul got a reputation as a funny man. It was so easy. You told them a simple truth in words of no more than three syllables, and the panic was on.

It got to the point (almost) where Paul would come in in the morning and say "Good morning, Charlie" and they would run up and down the office aisles laughing very loud and saying, "Did you hear what he said—ho ho ho ho—he said 'Good morning, Charlie.' "

He came to the office late, and left early, and spoke his mind and solved their problems, and it looked as if he could stay there forever, get more and more money, and more and more laughs.

Why, then, was there a small ogre perched between the vertebrae at the back of his neck, another at the small of his back?

He was back on the sun porch with his sister Helen, and something, he could no longer remember what, had struck them both so funny that they rocked back and forth, guffawing and wheezing and crying, their sides literally hurting, and the laughter would not stop.

Their mother came out and saw them, and she did not laugh, and she looked.

"Somebody's going to cry by nightfall," she said, and went away.

She always said that.

Another time Paul and his sister were laughing. They had not reached the point where they did not know what they were laughing about, and they were far from out of control. Something funny had happened and they were amused—immoderately—but not for their age, the kind of laughter you look at and envy when you yourself are grown up.

This was before Paul's father had died, and he was with Helen. Helen and Paul laughed together. Pearl and Helen laughed together, and once in a great while the three of them would go off together, but never did it happen when it was only Paul and Pearl.

Just what it was that was wrong between himself and Pearl he never knew when he was a little kid; he just knew it was a good idea to stay out of her way. Much much later, when she was a married woman and lived out of town, and they saw each other infrequently, it was by mutual consent that they stayed away from each other, and much later after that they concluded a wordless, cold truce and were able to behave to each other as civil strangers, and even like each other a bit, for short periods of time.

But this was long before that, about the time he had been graduated to knickerbockers. The sun was shining, and his sister sat on the cool red-leather-upholstered chair in the hall at the bottom of the stairs, and he lay spreadeagled on the bottom three stair treads, and they laughed.

Their mother came in. She had been on the phone. She looked at them. They stopped laughing.

"That was Fern Abeles," she said. "Mr. Abeles is dead."

Just about all they knew about him was his name.

They said they were sorry. Then they both remembered whatever it was that was so funny it had set them off.

Paul first, and then Helen, started to laugh again. Then stopped. And were ashamed. And waited for wrath.

Their mother looked at them.

And smiled.

And said, "Sometimes it affects people that way," and walked out of the room.

The way you went to McKinley Public School Number Two was up to the head of the hill, the way he walked with his sisters. And then without his sisters, going up the street with Manny, the kid two houses away, and whoever else fell into the line of march.

Paul was of the age where each morning there was a new alliance inside the group that straggled up and turned right on the main street to McKinley.

Each morning was like walking into unknown territory: was it to be himself and Manny against Keith, or Keith and his brother against Paul, or Paul and Keith against Manny and Keith's kid brother?

Along the way, at the corner of North Hudson and McKinley, a tall boy named Mike sort of fell in with the group.

By the time they were all going to the new junior high, Mike and Paul were best friends. Mike would be waiting for him in front of Paul's house—junior high was the other side of town—and now Paul's house was between Mike and school.

Paul was, given the chance, a sissy. He would rather read books than play tackle football, he would rather hunt bugs than stand in back of home plate and get a flung bat across his shins, he would rather pick wildflowers than count used contraceptives in Wilson Park.

Mike was the first person Paul knew who thought it was possible to do both. They went to the public library together and it was Mike who found a play called *Androcles and the Lion* (Androcles rhymed with yokels) and one day Mike told Paul that everybody jacked off. It was Paul who helped Mike tighten the spokes on Mike's brand-new secondhand bike painted, by Mike and Paul, the most hideous blue in the world.

Mike's old man was dead and he had two older sisters. Just like Paul.

The flow reversed itself again. Mike's house was between Paul and high school. Every morning Paul would climb the stone wall at the back of his backyard and walk along the hedge between Marcy Keller's house and the people who had no children and whose name he did not know. Then across the street and along the cement walk that led to the converted barn where the rich Quakers (he had heard the girl with sausage curls one day call her brother "Thou son of a bitch") kept their electric car.

Then past Mike's converted barn, where all that was housed was Mike's blue bicycle.

Into the back door. Mike was always eating a large bowl, a soup plate really, of farina with two raw eggs broken into it.

The first time Paul saw it he gagged, but after a while he got used to it.

They would say hello to each other, and maybe one of Mike's sisters would be there and say hello too.

And then, always, Mike's mother would take a look at Paul, and say, "Paul, you're so skinny," and she would put her arms around him and hug him and kiss him, until Paul thought he would die.

Of embarrassment or love, he never knew which.

One day he and Mike were wandering down in the village—in Paul's part of the United States where the stores are is called the village, in the West it's called downtown—and they passed the movie house near the railroad tracks. This was an odd little independent theater, not in the same league as the local Proctor's which had vaudeville, and chocolate-vending machines on the backs of the seats. It must have been there for a very long time, for the name of it was the Bunny, after a moonfaced comedian of the silent days. There was a sign posted above the cash window stating that positively no one under sixteen would be admitted, so Mike and Paul promptly agreed to cut school the next day and see the dirty movie at the Bunny.

This they did, except that the movie turned out not to be dirty. It was a silent, *The Cabinet of Dr. Caligari,* and it scared the pluperfect piss out of both of them, and became a permanent part of Paul's dream life right up to this very day.

They were disappointed that it was not dirty, standing as they were more in need of erotic fodder than any more terror, but they agreed it was a hell of a movie and well worth twenty-five cents. How it had found its way to the Bunny was a puzzle they did not attempt to solve then and it remained a lone expedition into art for the theater, which went right back to Tom Mix for the rest of their adolescence.

Another time, much later, Paul saw *The Maltese Falcon* and it was the first of a series of movies spoiled for him by simple lust. Certainly there has never been a more desirable female than Mary Astor in that movie and, despite making no sense at all of the plot then or since, Paul understood clearly what Mary Astor was proposing toward the end of the film when she said she would do anything Bogart wanted if he wouldn't send her to jail. Paul would willingly, nay eagerly, have compounded this felony, like any red-blooded American boy, and that damn fool Bogart turned into a scoutmaster and sent her to the jug. It was beyond belief, and the only fake thing in the movie.

Just recently Paul saw *The Graduate*, where the tastiest-looking dish since Dolores Costello, a mature Anne Bancroft, is doing a young man the exquisite compliment of banging him and listening to his asinine reflections on the world, and this besotted fool turns her down to couple with a pudding-faced girl of nineteen. As far as Paul was concerned, the boy was a clod, and for the rest of the movie he didn't give a damn what happened to him.

But before that, quite a few years, Paul saw a movie called *The Taste of Honey* and came away thinking it one of the very best moom pitchas he had ever seen. His older son, then about sixteen, had a date one afternoon, and for a wonder inquired about the cinema, and Paul recommended he lose no time in seeing this movie.

His son and his date took off, and were back in half an hour, his son bearing that awful wounded look of the young when reminded of their youth. It seems the theater had decided no one under eighteen could see this innocent love story. On the other side of town they could have seen Kirk Douglas bare his teeth and cut Tony Curtis's head off, with real blood flowing in the scuppers, but this one, no.

Paul's hair caught on fire, and he phoned the movie house and treated the manager to fifteen minutes of abuse, suggesting that it was his business to decide what movies his son saw, not any goddam movie-house manager, and when he paused for breath, the poor bastard on the other end of the phone agreed with him and asked if he could not have the pleasure of his son's company at the movie, on the house.

Sometimes Paul thinks that was his finest hour as a parent, and he wishes he could forget that neither his son nor his son's date thought very much of the movie.

Paul's mother's brother came to live with them. He was a teacher, and he read books. He could ice-skate, he could catch and throw a ball, but he could not drive a car any more than Paul's father could. He was a good-looking man, and his hair was wavy, and Paul's mother said that he and Paul were very much alike.

He didn't talk much. It was only slowly that Paul found out he was the brother that all the sisters had sacrificed themselves for. It was his mother's family that was always going around sacrificing themselves for others, and it took Paul half a lifetime to find out that when somebody sacrifices himself for somebody else, it adds up quite often that the person sacrificed for is the one who is sacrificed.

What made Uncle Vinnie a real hero in Paul's eyes was the knowledge that he had been a chemist on a sugar plantation in Cuba, and had walked out because of the intolerable exploitation of the cane cutters. He found this out when he was fifteen, and at twenty-two first began to wonder if staying there and doing something about it might have been even more heroic. At twenty-five, Paul having had some experience of doing something about exploitation, Uncle Vinnie turned out not to be a hero or a bum in Paul's eyes.

But this happened long before all that, when Paul was five or six. A whole mess of kids was gathered on the front lawn, doing very little, when Uncle Vinnie walked out. He stooped over and picked up a penny from the flower bed, and showed it to them. "You're very inattentive kids," he said, and bent over and picked up a nickel.

All the kids clustered around him and followed him around the lawn like chicks after a hen, and first one kid, then another, found a coin. They went wild, money for free, and it was a hysterical explosion. They ran around and picked up money, and jostled each other and Uncle Vinnie, and it really never occurred to any of them that it was odd there was money only where Uncle Vinnie had been. It spiraled up, and then quit as cold as it had started.

The group broke up, and Uncle Vinnie sat on the front lawn and talked quietly to Paul's father.

Paul's mother called Paul inside. "You shouldn't have let him do that, Paul. He doesn't have much money."

"Do what?" Paul said.

"Oh, you knew that Uncle Vinnie was dropping that money."

He hadn't known. What was so strange about a grownup doing things that a kid couldn't do, like finding money?

He shouldn't have let him do it. How do you stop a grownup from doing anything in the world he wants to do?

And forty-odd years later, how could anyone be so stinking about so much delirium bought for a grand total of, say, sixty-three cents?

The trouble (one of the troubles) in being six years old is that damn near everything is taller than you are.

After Paul found that once he got to the top of the hill his sisters were so far ahead of him he was as good as alone, it got to be an open compact that they would go to school without him, which was for them a cinch—and he would go to school without them, which was a little different.

First, there was the ambush at Jackson and North Pelham. Two kids, one his age, one older, lived there. The only name they had was Gool and Dick. Gool and Dick were the kind of kids who enjoyed hitting other kids. And tripping them. And throwing horse apples at them. There didn't seem to be any malice about it, nor were there appointed victims. They twisted your arm up behind your back until the sound of popping tendons could be heard at Wilson Park. They did this the way other kids said hello.

The question was, were they busy with another kid as Paul approached, or was he it, or were Gool and Dick there at all this morning?

If you got past there, there was what he did not yet know as the Hound of the Baskervilles, all the way from North Pelham to Curtis. Paul on one side of the hedge, the Hound on the other, black and huge and red-eyed, and slavering and baying like another hound he didn't know yet—the Hound of Hell.

When you're eight years old it is not unusual to wet your pants a little, from time to time. Paul was usual.

The next block offered no unusual hazards to a damp and terrified Paul.

The girls went in the girls' entrance. The boys went in the boys' entrance. There were minor-league Gools and Dicks. There were friends—well, they had been friends yesterday.

And when you were all through with that, when the lady teacher with the bun decided your nails were clean enough, when you had the handkerchiefs for show and for blow, and the shoes considered shined enough, and you were not tardy—there was geography.

Paul looked at a map. He did not understand anything about it at all. They had left out a part of his brain. The fact is, he didn't know what a map was.

Or is. The whole world consists of right turns and left turns to Paul, and in place of Gool and Dick there are the men who may be muggers.

Paul's mother had been born in the United States and had grown up in farm country in Pennsylvania. Paul's father had been born in Russia and had not seen the United States until he was sixteen. He had clawed his way up and out of the Lower East Side.

To Paul's mother this meant that basically she was not Jewish, and Paul's father was. They were both Jewish, but she was so only because she chose to be. Paul's father, of course, had no choice.

To Paul's mother then, the whole world, animate and inanimate, was divided into Jewish and not Jewish, the Gentile person or object in each case being clearly the better, and to be used.

Paul grew up in a world in which not only people were Jewish and Gentile, but things. Their phone number, a Hillcrest exchange, was good and high-class and Gentile. Oakwood was a Jewish exchange and much less honorable. Their milk company was Jewish, and the other one not. (This had nothing to do with the personnel of the milk companies, which were both Anglo-Irish.) Paul's family was affluent and owned either a Dodge or a Cadillac, well-established non-Jewish automobiles. Buicks were Jewish, and pointy shoes, and Social Tea crackers. Drinking milk from a cup was Jewish, which was odd considering that his father's very Jewish and very low-class relatives drank tea from a glass.

Curly hair was Jewish, the color purple, and high shoes with cloth tops.

Horn-rimmed glasses were Gentile and okay, ditto collie dogs, whereas rimless glasses and bull terriers were clearly Hebraic. The *Globe* was a Jewish newspaper, the *Sun* uncircumcised.

Paul and his sisters swallowed this whole. His father had long since abandoned his wife and children to their own devices. His older sister particularly absorbed this arrant and vicious nonsense and went so far as to consider herself some sort of princess.

That a mother is able so to influence her own children is perhaps not too surprising. What made Paul's mother one of the truly brilliant myth makers of all time is that she managed to convince the whole town that the family was something so special, it did the village great honor that the Marranes chose to live among them in amity, and so democratically.

Between his sisters, the highest praise of a girl's appearance was that she was not at all Jewish-looking. Paul was satisfactory until the age of fourteen, at which point his penis and nose both began to grow. His clyde

was, for the moment, his own affair, but his quite re-
markable eagle beak was a family concern. They
twisted his head so that it shone in the light and said
what a pity.

Dipping while dancing, which his cousins did with
skill, was Jewish. Dresses that came to points at the
hem, two-color shoes (except saddle shoes), socks with
clocks, the singing of Caruso and anything sweet and
sour, it turned out, were too. So were prunes, button-
hooks, and any college in New York City.

It is a long time gone now, and Paul has accepted
for years that what makes a Jew is somebody calling
him one (proving his mother right) and the ancient
truth that a Jew is just like everyone else, only more so.

And yet . . . and yet.

He never wears pointy shoes, he knows way deep
down that he is Jewish only because he chooses to be,
and the fact that he chooses to be does him great honor.

There they sat, the three of them, Manny, Keith, and Paul, on the stone wall at the foot of Paul's back yard. For once the three of them were in a lasting alliance, and it was a pleasant and important occasion. They were choosing names.

At their age, a nickname was really more important than a real name because it was the way your peers spoke of you and to you, and the wrong name could leave you scarred and bleeding. Somewhere today, in the dark reaches of the night, a fifty-two-year-old man is sleeping badly because he was known on his block as Juicy. The solemn fellow who comes into Zucca's every day, and drinks too much all by himself at the end of the bar, can partly blame it on the fact that someone, when he was six, tagged him Four-Eyes.

It was getting a little stormy out for the three of them; they were starting to call Manny Bigass, Keith being a Junior was on the precipice of Junie, and Paul, being a sissy, was being called Sissy. Very well, if they chose for themselves, and all agreed, they'd be able to put it over on everybody, maybe.

It is impossible to remember now how the names were arrived at—it would have been a little difficult even then to find any logic in it—but after a very long time Manny became Chuck, Keith Mitch, and Paul Biscuit. (To make this absolutely clear, Manny's middle name was not Charles, Keith's last name was not Mitchell, and Paul's mother did not bake biscuits.)

They tried them on for sound, once agreed, and although the names were new and embarrassing, they liked the notion.

You could say it was then that Paul first discovered the importance of words.

Still later, he discovered the power of the sobriquet. One summer at a camp where all was heartiness and athletics and being hit with canoe paddles, he found himself sharing in the arm-twisting and general nastiness of Manny's older brother, who was an apprentice counselor there.

He was built on the general lines of a football center, and he was one of those people like Gool and Dick, who liked to hit. At that time Paul weighed eighty-five pounds (as they used to say at that time, wringing wet after a meal of doorknobs). In any event, it seemed so often true that those who liked to hit didn't mind so much being hit if they could get their own licks in. There is a general fiction that bullies, once faced, blubber and squeak, as in *Tom Brown's School Days*, but there was not, and is not, a word of truth in this theory. It is true, however, that people like Paul, who do not like to hit, do not like being hit. It hurts. So physical action was out.

There was a small child in the camp, torn away from his mother too young, who wandered around, lisping, drooling, wetting his pants, his eyes unfocused. He was so pitiful that no one took out after him. In truth, he had been adopted by the whole camp as a sort of sub-human mascot, was made much of, had unheard-of privileges, and was a pet in every respect but collar and leash.

Paul carefully taught him to call Manny's older brother "The Bull" every time he saw him. When the rest of the small fry saw how red in the face Manny's older brother got when the small spitty child called him that, they encouraged and helped him encounter Manny's older brother at frequent intervals.

The Bull came to hit Manny much less often, and to twist Paul's arm not at all.

In Paul's office there is a team of account executives known generally as Peter Pan and Tinkerbelle, an over-jovial art director as Hohoho, and one of the executive creative geniuses as The Aristocrat, from the dirty story of the same name.

To a marked extent, Paul's nickname is Paul, or at least to date it's the only one he's heard.

Paul's mother was very large. She was tall, she was fat (not according to her, in her view she had large bones, but if she did, you'd have had a hell of a time finding them under all that fat), and she had a quality Paul was never to encounter again until Picasso's classical ladies-on-a-beach department. She occupied a hell of a lot of space. When she was in a room, there didn't seem to be much space left, and it was a little like the movies in which a submarine crew is left with thirty seconds' worth of air. She had another quality: as some objects give off light, Paul's mother gave off dark. She entered a room and all the light bulbs shrank to fifteen watts.

Paul's father was small, and his sisters were one small, one medium, but to Paul they were all huge.

He was the smallest breathing thing in the house, and it was always Paul's image of himself that, given a good sturdy handle, he would have made a serviceable overnight bag.

When he had a dog, one of the delights was that Paul was bigger than the dog, but the dog was taken away. He hunted bugs as much because he could dominate them as for any other reason.

And then he discovered models. Model ships, model planes, model wagons, anything at all so long as it was the tiniest of its kind. He built them and if they were not perfect they went into the hell box of the coal furnace.

Among his marbles was the smallest realie in the world, and a ball bearing that was the smallest steelie in the world.

He found a very small knife, and one day a kid brought to school a little gun about an inch long that shot rice grains and Paul bargained until it was his.

In the gum, cockamamie, and magazine store on the wrong side of the town there was the smallest pencil sharpener in the world. It sold for three cents. It was a long letter U made of wire and across the open end a scrap of knife blade.

Not six weeks ago Paul hooked from his office three plastic file boxes for three-by-five cards, the bottom black, the top clear, and he now has three of the smallest greenhouses in the world growing rectangles of moss.

It doesn't seem to make any difference now that Paul is six feet tall. He has two sons who are both over six feet.

It was the first summer he had ever spent by the seashore. There was a little house, and the sidewalks were made of board, and he could walk down the sidewalk by himself until he reached a stringpiece, very old and smelling of tar. His mother was ordinarily very cautious but for some reason (he could never figure out much consistency in her ukases—it was she, of all people, who had taught him how to dry corn silk and smoke it) he was allowed out on the stringpiece by himself with a tarred cord, and a brass spreader and two big fluke hooks and a dime for sandworms, and he spent what seemed like whole days there. It was easy to bait the hooks, because a sandworm was such a mess to begin with and clawed so nauseatingly at his hand that he could get mad and stick the hook through as if he were destroying an enemy. He hauled up fluke after fluke, and they were such a mess with the one white side and the one speckled side and the two eyes on top, that they, too, could die without causing him much pain.

They were lousy to eat, dry and muddy to the taste at the same time, but his mother and father said they liked them.

It was an extraordinary summer. His father got very sunburned, and his father and mother talked to each other and even went for walks together in the evening.

Helen learned to swim in the offshore surf, and came in second in a race, and Pearl wore silk stockings rolled to her knee on the beach—it was the law—and played the ukulele. His sisters made tuna-fish sandwiches for breakfast, toasting the bread and the tuna fish on the sloping side of the electric toaster, and they made some for him, too.

And one day, astonishingly, there was a dog. It was a fox terrier, and it was his. It was a wonder. It had four legs and a tail and it was warm and his and it snoozed in the sun next to him on the stringpiece and walked home at his heels.

Like many terriers, it shook a lot, and it had mange. He didn't know, and buried his face in the dog's flanks, and then it was part of his job to rub some sulphur-smelling stuff onto the dog, and he could no longer bury his face in its breathing side, but it still followed him and sat next to him on the stringpiece, and it was his dog.

The extraordinary summer drew to a close. It was on the day they left that he found the dog was part of the summer, to be left behind with the fluke hooks and the spreader and the cork floats he had found on the beach, and the dried horseshoe crabs, and the seaweed that you could pop between your fingers.

He tried everything he knew and, as usual, lost.

One day in the winter his sister Pearl said something at the dinner table and then clapped her hand over her mouth. She had heard from one of her friends who lived at the beach all year long. The dog had been run over and killed.

They all looked at her, and Paul looked down at the tablecloth.

They were expecting him to cry, and he wanted to, sort of.

"What's the use?" he said to himself, for the very first time.

One of the things you could find, and catch, in the ponds in Fisher's Woods was polliwogs. They looked like little black seeds, and Paul got a jam jar full and took them home.

It turned out to be one of the days when his mother was—remembering, he thought later, being a country girl—on his side, and she got a shallow cut-glass bowl and allowed him to place it on the bamboo-legged, cane-topped, sun-porch table.

It is important to remember that these were not tadpoles—which are gray and grossly overstuffed—but polliwogs which are small and black and shiny and move quickly.

His sisters were having a party that night, and he heard the phonograph playing "Rio Rita" and "Dardanella" and "Jericho" and running down and speeding up, and he went to sleep wondering if it was true that polliwogs turned into frogs and what would he keep the frogs in and what would he feed them. He knew he was safe on the polliwogs because there was a small envelope of ant eggs left over from the goldfish.

In the morning he went downstairs and first thing went to the sun porch. No bowl. No polliwogs.

His mother was in the kitchen. She didn't know anything about it. He pounded up the stairs and woke his sisters.

Oh, sure. They had been dancing, and the bowl had fallen off the table and had broken.

"But the polliwogs," he was screaming, "didn't you even try to pick them up?"

Helen said later in the day that they had tried, but he knew perfectly well that the idea had never occurred to them.

This, too, was to be true all Paul's life. Things which mattered a great deal to him meant damn all to most of the people he knew.

There was a boy named Jerry Principal. It was in the sixth grade and he showed up one day, and he talked differently from everybody else. It was Midwestern, though Paul did not know that then.

He was a solemn boy, and he spoke slowly and solemnly, and moved with deliberation. It was as if he thought before he did anything. What eventually came out of his mouth was no wiser than what was being uttered by his peers, but the pause between the thought and the statement made what he said seem much more important than it really was.

Instead of being pecked to death, he was treated with circumspection. At the close of the school day, he disappeared. He never walked home with anyone, and no one seemed to know where he lived. He simply ceased to be at three o'clock and came into being again the next morning.

One day he was standing in the schoolyard, waiting for the opening bell to ring. Quite casually he clasped his hands behind his back, and equally casually lifted them clasped over the head and right on down in front of him, so that he now stood with his hands clasped in front of him.

He did it twice.

"He's double-jointed," some kid said, and in Paul's mind that meant just what it said; where everybody else had one joint, Jerry Principal had two.

It was a two-day, three-day, all-term wonder.

Then one day Jerry Principal sat at his desk, folding a piece of paper. When he was through, he had a little bird, and as he pulled the beak and the tail between his hands, the wings flapped.

He never said anything about either of these accomplishments, he just did them.

Paul asked him to his birthday party, and at the appointed time Jerry appeared at the front door and held out his hand. In it was a small package. It contained a two-bladed knife with both blades pivoted at the same end, and a big bolster, on which were printed the words GENUINE BARLOW. Just like in Mark Twain.

Paul thought Jerry Principal was a wonder then. Now, almost half a century later, Paul still thinks so, although he has no idea where or what or who Jerry now is.

He was one of the few people in the world who didn't talk about things. Jerry did them.

Paul was in high school and they were reading *The Odyssey*, and they came to the part about Ulysses in the cave of Polyphemus. Ulysses told what Paul thought then and thinks now is a pretty hokey joke, about Polyphemus asking who was there, and Ulysses saying "No man," but there was something about Ulysses' exit from the cave that filled Paul's nose with the scent of damp wool, and traveling gently upside down, and there in the class he was back in the house of his childhood.

He knew for sure that there had been a large gentle collie dog next door. He could prove it, because there was a snapshot of him in a sailor suit, thin and pale and trussed up, standing by the dog. Just the way people have changed, so have collie dogs. Lassie's head was not shaped like a grape seed, and the haunches were not carved away hollow like a borzoi, the way collies are today. This was a large, pillowy, thick dog, and there had been a time in his life when Paul had thought Lassie was his mother.

He had talked to Lassie, he had buried his face in the brown and white gently smelly fur, and, sitting there in the high school class, he was pretty sure he had come under Lassie, locked his arms and legs around her as she stood, hiding his face in her belly, and Lassie had waddled slowly with Paul like a burr underneath.

But it is very hard to be sure what is in your own unconscious, and what is in the collective unconscious, and Paul thinks now: maybe Homer had his own problem.

Paul turned from a beast into a human the same way as everyone else: he learned to read.

It was a mixed blessing. Once he found that books were full of people, it was all right to indulge his shyness, and stay away more from real people.

For some time the books around the house, which were very few, and the books around the block—*The Boy Allies, The Motor Boys, Tom Swift, Mark Tidd, Roy Somebody or Other and His Beeline Hike, Baseball Joe*—were enough for him, and then he discovered the public library. It was very far from his house, and had the Basic Librarian who knows that the true function of books is to be on shelves in the proper alphabetical and subject order, with cards in pockets. There was a rule in the library: you were allowed, as a child, two fiction and two nonfiction for two weeks with no renewal, and if you were late you were sent to an underground dungeon and had a talk with Torquemada.

All over this town in those years small boys and girls

—and some not so small—woke up in the middle of the night with the inside sweats and heavy palpitations as they faced the ceiling and realized that their liberry books were overdue, and that they faced total financial annihilation.

This particular library was a block through, and had two entrances, one on each street. One was for adults, one for children, and there was a connecting corridor inside for those few parents who went to the library and got books out for their kids. It was also possible, then, for a kid to creep down the hall, face the adults' librarian and say that his mother or sister or father had asked him to pick up a copy of *Badgirlbyviñadelmar* or *Audels' Electricians' Guide*. It was possible to ask this. It was seldom possible to brazen it through, inasmuch as the library certainly did not have a copy of *Bad Girl*, or *Office Wife*. Or even *Jennie Gerhardt*.

But one way or another, Paul got his two fiction and two nonfiction and trudged back home with three under his arm and one under his nose, or later three strapped on the rear fender of his bicycle and one on the handle bars. And started back to the library the minute he was on the last ten pages of the fourth book —fiction or nonfiction as the case might be.

In order to get a book out again—they were all un-renewable—you had to return it, wait until it was back on the shelves, and get it out before some other kids did. If the book happened to be *The Cat of Bubastis* this might take a kid two weeks, grownup time—to a kid, that's half a year—to get it out again.

It wasn't until they moved to the city that Paul dis-covered Fourth Avenue and for many years all his pocket money went for secondhand books, mostly from the dime-and-quarter stalls in front of the stores. In those days there was treasure to be had for a pittance on Fourth Avenue and his library grew. As he got wealthier, he found his way into the bookstores and for years he had what his friends considered a parlor trick. Someone would say he was looking for, say, a copy of Trollope's *The Three Clerks* and Paul would say, "Third shelf from the bottom about halfway across. Left side of the store as you go in. It's the store on the west side of Fourth between Eighth and Ninth with the copy of Stubbs's *Anatomy of the Horse* in the window. It's marked seventy-five cents, but you can probably get it for half a buck." You had to be very cautious about saying what you could get a book for, because there was an eccentric bookdealer on Fourth who did the damnedest things. In those days it was quite clearly understood that a marked price was just the beginning: it was where the haggling started, expected by the bookdealers and allowed for in the price. But this one bookdealer was different. One day Paul had been standing in his shop and another customer was busy rooting through the chess books, a specialty of the store. He found one, and it was obvious from his expression that it was a treasure he'd been searching for for years. "How much do you want for this?" he asked the dealer. "What's it marked?" "Three and a half dollars"—which was a lot of money for a book in those days. "That's what I want for it, then," said the dealer, "and each time you ask it's going to cost you half a dollar more." "No, really," said the customer. "Four," said the dealer. "Oh, come on," the customer said. "We've always been able to do business before. I've been coming here for a year." "Then you should know that when I say something I mean it. Four and a half."

And it ended with the customer paying five and a half dollars for a book marked three and a half.

But in the other stores it was like an Eastern bazaar, and Paul often walked out with books for half the marked price.

Sometimes Paul would look for a book for years, and long after he no longer wanted a certain book he would see it for sale and buy it just to have the victory of the chase. One day he found a store that was selling out and in it was a twelve-volume set of a Victorian edition of Wood's *Animate Creation* with colored plates, at fifty cents the volume, and like a damned fool he bought only the volume on sea creatures and lugged it home, and spent the rest of his life regretting he hadn't had the six bucks for the complete set.

Another day he found a treasure he had originally encountered in his hometown public library, a volume called *The Boy Mechanic*, with plans for everything from a buckboard to a Chanute glider, and he took that home and planned one day to build a glider of spruce and duck and fly the way he did in his dreams.

Paul became addicted to books the way some people are addicted to morphine: on his night table there had to be the book he was reading, the book he planned to read after the book he was reading, and at least three books beyond that in the chain.

By the time he was married, there were books on the night tables, the coffee table, in bookcases and closets and tottery piles all over the floor. Occasionally he would have a great clean-out and get rid of a dozen or so, and in the months to come quite a few times he would buy back a book he had sold a few months ago.

When he became a writer, he made clear to whatever editor he was dealing with at whatever publishing house that part of his contract was the unwritten clause that he could haul away a copy of any book the publisher published.

He never fussed with the nonsense of book collecting. Bookplates and a first edition meant nothing one way or the other to him, particularly since, with most of the books he bought, the rare item would have been a second edition.

His wife learned to live the life of a bibliomaniac's wife, and his two sons caught the fever and amassed their own libraries.

It amounts to this: that practically no day passes that Paul does not buy a book for fear that the evening will come and he will have nothing to read.

Paul, now, will not buy an overcoat until he sees if a book will fit in the pocket; his night table looks like an outdoor stall from a secondhand bookstore. And it is literally true that on one trip to the West Coast, when he stayed for a week, he had to buy a canvas valise to bring home the books he had bought there.

And the glider and *The Boy Mechanic*. He is looking for a copy of it right now, and five years ago he went to a town upstate and attempted to learn to fly a sailplane. In order to do that, he had to learn to fly a Piper Cub, and the day he stepped out of the Cub and looked through the wrong half of his bifocal lenses, missed the step, and went on his face was the first clue he had that he was no longer a boy, a mechanic, or a glider pilot.

At night he still dreams of flying, and some nights he is sure the flying means fucking, and some nights it means flying.

A couple of times during the year, usually at the Jewish holidays, Paul's whole family would go up to Uncle Selig's house. This was his father's older brother, and Uncle Selig was poor and they lived in the Bronx, in a two-family house. Paul's grandmother lived there. She was a small crookback gnome with no teeth and no English, and Paul would kiss her prune-wrinkled cheek, and they would sit across from each other and she would say, "Naaa, naaa," and utter incomprehensible things in Yiddish, and Paul would stare at her sunken dead-white face and—not knowing what a sheitel was—wonder how such an old lady could have such shining, smooth black hair.

There were always more people than the rooms could hold, and a lot of noise, and Aunt Hagar was in the kitchen, and when the meal was about to be served stood against the wall of the dining room watching to see when anyone's plate was empty, at which point she heaped it again.

Uncle Selig looked then the way Charlie Ruggles looks now, now that his hair and mustache were white, and he had very red cheeks.

But the most amazing thing about the whole visit— this was true even when it was not a holiday gathering —was that Paul's father turned into a prince of the blood the minute he crossed the threshold.

His coat was taken from him, he was ushered into the best chair, delicacies were brought to him; there was a new bottle of three-star Hennessy or some smuggled slivovitz.

He was asked questions as he sat on the throne; his slightest utterance called for a wagging of heads, and the minute he spoke, total silence prevailed.

Paul shared in the glory.

Now, when Paul goes to his sister Helen's house, it is a bad day if there isn't pickled herring, or chopped liver, or the very best gin, and when he makes a joke, they laugh.

Paul's father was rich; he could not drive a car; and he was sick. Not everybody had a car then, and Paul's family had what very few people in his hometown had, a car and a chauffeur.

Since Paul's father was sick and stayed at home, the car was very often available to him and his sisters for transportation to school. His mother struggled between her impulse to make them all walk to school (because it was good for them, and because she as a girl had been poor) and the impulse to show the town what a classy rich family they were, possessing a car and a chauffeur. The chauffeur's name was Jimmy, and Paul's mother really said, from time to time, "Home, James."

So sometimes Paul and his sisters walked to school and sometimes they rode in a Cadillac touring car with isinglass side windows and Jimmy in front.

One morning when Paul was about seven years old, it was one of the mornings they were to ride to school in the car, drop Paul and his friend Manny at McKinley

Public School Number Two, and then take his sisters on off to high school.

It was raining, but not much, and as usual Paul's nose was running, not much, but enough to insure him a ride.

In front of McKinley School was the crossing cop. His first or last name was Perry and he was therefore wittily called Perry Winkle (after the comic strip), and one day he had plugged a run-over cat with his pistol and was thereafter known, even more wittily, as Brave Perry Winkle.

The car stopped, Manny got out and started crossing the street and Paul followed him, and then something big and black came tearing down the street and knocked Paul up in the air. He landed about eight feet down the road.

The big black thing was a touring car with out-of-town plates, and in addition to smashing up Paul's left leg (the bumper) and his right arm (the pavement) it neatly took Manny's rubber right off his shoe, which was to bring him considerable fame in the days to come.

Brave Perry Winkle and Jimmy the chauffeur and the man who was driving the car and his sisters and a gang of other people got Paul to the hospital. His leg was broken (you could see that) and an intern kept moving his arm around and asking him if it hurt until Paul fainted.

In the months to come there was on Paul a cast from nape to clyde, his arm up in salute, and a cast from clyde to toe on his leg, and wheel chairs and crutches and a baking of his arm in a small oven made of toaster wire and chicken wire and plaster of Paris. A mosquito got under the shirt cast, and his toes turned to cheese in the stocking cast.

The driver of the car came to the hospital and asked him if he liked to go fishing and promised to come back with a genuine split-bamboo fishing rod and take Paul fishing in *his* hometown, and then he blew town that afternoon and was never heard of again.

His entire public school class wrote him nearly identical letters about the class party. Friends tried his crutches, and Manny pushed him in the wheel chair very fast, and one night, right after the shirt cast was taken off, Paul woke up in the middle of the night and saw his white, dead, shrunken arm and cried for a long time, without noise.

Paul's mother never, in the next five years, stopped saying it was Pearl's fault, or Jimmy the chauffeur's fault, or Brave Perry Winkle's fault, or Manny's fault, and somehow or other none of them ever liked Paul very much after that.

Paul now cannot wear a suit or a shirt the way it comes from a store (the arm was broken in the growing bud) and this irritates him, and he has a tendency to think first that everything is always somebody's fault, and then, later on, that nothing is anybody's fault, and then, still later, that neither of the statements is true.

"Are you sure you don't have to go to the toilet before we leave?" Paul's mother used to say.

"I don't think so," Paul would say, as soon as he learned to talk that well.

"We won't be back home for some time," his mother would say. "Maybe you'd better go to make sure."

"I don't have to go," Paul would say, and his mother would say, "If you're not sure you can hold on until we come home, you'd better go now."

Paul learned by age six to pee on command.

Paul now puts in a lot of time walking between where he is sitting and whatever toilet is nearest.

He is never sure he can bear to sit in the dentist's chair or the barber's chair until the teeth are filled or the hairs cut.

Waiting rooms in railway depots and airlines are way stations to Paul, and his wife has never had a second cup of coffee at a restaurant in peace and quiet.

He has two sons whose bladders are cast of solid brass, and they make trains and planes at the last minute, and sweat very little.

Paul learned to say his prayers, "Now I lay me down to sleep, I pray the Lord my soul to keep; if I should die before I wake, I pray the Lord my soul to take," by rote, as separate syllables meaning absolutely nothing except another thing you had to do because somebody said you had to do it.

A little later on, he learned to add "God bless Mother and Father and Pearl and Helen" and then he learned to add names onto that so he could postpone a little longer getting in bed, and having the light turned out.

At some stage in his adult life, long after he had ceased to say this or any other prayer, he realized one day what the words signified and his blood ran cold.

As he was getting on for thirteen, it seemed he had to prepare for something called a bar mitzvah, which included going to see a malodorous man in the new building with automatic elevators on the other side of town, and learn Hebrew.

Up until then, the Jewish religion had consisted of

going to Sunday school in a reformed temple, where the words to "Ein Kelohenu" and other madrigals were printed out phonetically in English on large white oil-cloth sheets suspended from a golden-oak stand. There were also periods of sitting on a folding chair next to Vivian Volk and pointing out to each other the dirty parts in the Bible.

But now that he was to be bar mitzvahed, he started attending, on Saturdays, services at the orthodox shul. This was quite different. In the first place, since it was Saturday he no longer got money to buy the Sunday *American* and read the section that was lavishly illustrated and, it seemed, every week had a story headed "Society Woman Gives Dinner Party for Gorillas." For kicks now, he had to be content with the corset ads in the *New York Times* rotogravure section.

It was, however, exciting to wear a tallis, and when they opened the solid-gold doors of the Ark of the Torah and brought out the scroll with the little gold bells on top, laid it down, and chanted from it, he was scared and delighted.

The sessions with the malodorous man were another thing. He was taught to read the Hebrew, but not what it meant, and that was enough for a while.

Every Jewish boy who comes from a not deeply religious family is bar mitzvahed *for* someone. For the sake of Uncle Max, or Grandpa, or Mother's Granduncle Peretz in Detroit.

Paul was being bar mitzvahed for his grandmother. And then Paul's father died, and he was being bar mitzvahed for the memory of his father—who had turned socialist-atheist when Paul was four years old.

This meant that the portion of the Torah Paul was to chant was changed, and the smelly man breathed all over him on a new piece of unintelligibility. Paul asked the man what it meant, and the man, in effect, told him it was none of his business.

Paul went for a long walk after school that day and stopped off at the rabbi's house, a thing he had never done before. The rabbi was home and Paul told him what was on his mind, and the rabbi showed him a limited edition of *Beowulf* and told him about fine printing and gave him some tea, and Paul went away perfectly convinced that the rabbi thought religion was one of the biggest crocks in the world.

He did his bar mitzvah, and said kaddish for his father for a few years, and then one summer he went to see the rabbi again. It had been a very bad time for Paul and he had prayed very hard, and he knew then that if there was any comfort to be gotten from religion he, Paul, would never get it. He told the rabbi this, and the rabbi gave him a slightly used stamp album and a packet of stamps and showed him a limited edition of *The Ballad of Reading Gaol.*

Many years later a radio actor, later to be black-listed and destroyed, was sitting at a bar near Paul and said that he had formed a new organization, "The National Conference Against Christians and Jews." Paul asked if he could become a member.

The other day Paul met the actor as he was walking home, and Paul told him this: "I have a slogan for our organization. 'If God's not dead, let's kill him.'"

As with all small boys, haircuts were an ordeal for Paul. What made them cruel and unusual punishment was that Jimmy the chauffeur was delegated to drag him downtown and get him shorn. Now Jimmy was a gambler. He would bet on anything. Which raindrops would course down a windowpane first, how long it would take for a fly to land on a lump of sugar, craps, poker, the horses—anything. In Paul's hometown Gene the Barber had his shop directly across the square from the City Hall. Gene was indeed a barber, but he was also indeed the local bookie and proprietor of a crap game that floated no farther than the back room of the barbershop.

Later on Paul on his own would have gone to the shop of Sam Mahler the Square Deal Man, which was just this side of the railroad tracks and had the largest collection of girlie magazines in town. Paul would sit there looking at Lili Damita leaning way over and he was at the boiling point by the time Sam Mahler was ready for him. In those days a kid in a barbershop waited until all the men were taken care of, but no adolescent ever complained as long as he could live in Lili's cleavage.

But in his younger days it was Jimmy's choice of barbershops and that always meant Gene's. There was one chair. Gene would cut a hair or two, wander into the back room and pick up his share of the table stakes, pad out and cut a few more hairs. If Jimmy's luck was holding in the back room, it sometimes took as much as an hour for Gene to cut Paul's hair; and if on the other hand Jimmy's luck was bad, it often took as much as an hour for Gene to cut Paul's hair. Eventually the haircut would be over and Gene would drench him in a cloud of vile perfume. Jimmy would come out of the unventilated, smoky back room smelling like an old cuspidor and they would ride home in the mingled scent.

His mother's parting instructions to him were always the same: don't let him use the clippers too high in back. And Gene always used the clippers too high in back no matter what Paul said, and when he got home she would tsk-tsk about the back and brush the waves back just behind his forehead.

When Paul went to college, it was the era of the crew cut and a great relief to Paul, who had his hair cut short all over, never had to brush it, and washed it every day he took a shower.

Paul's boys come home from college now with great masses of tangled hair, and most of the people Paul sees seem to have more hair than people used to. Several times he has been utterly confused in a barber chair. What is a razor cut? What does the barber mean when he asks if he wants his sideburns dark or light? What in heaven's name did the barber in Chicago mean when he asked him what he wanted done about his eyebrows?

In an effort to keep abreast of modern developments in the field of head hair, Paul went to a hotel barber shop in his neighborhood and a young man—before Paul knew what he was about—cut some hair, shampooed it, razor-cut it, put a hair net on it and sprayed it, went over it with a hot-air blower and made sure the waves were in place, and sent him out into the afternoon with his hair set and he poorer by five and a half bucks.

The shocking thing about it all is that Paul liked it very much and is trying to get up the courage—and the scratch—to go back again. The barber, for the first time in Paul's tonsorial life, did not use the clippers too high in the back. How pleased Paul's mother would have been to see it.

After a certain length of time it became clear to Paul that the broken arm was not going to grow as his unbroken arm was growing, and he would have one arm shorter than the other.

There was a lot of talk with a lot of different doctors; there was a certain amount of argle-bargle about always carrying packages with the short arm; but there came one day when he saw the miracle-worker doctor.

He also turned out to be an honest man. "Tell you what I'll do," he said to Paul and his mother, "I'll break the other one and set it wrong."

Paul did not then and does not now know what sensation his mother felt at this statement. To Paul it was a blessed relief.

The arm was a different thing. He swam in circles. He rowed boats in circles. He could not chin himself easily. He felt somehow he was like the Kaiser, who had a withered arm.

Whatever it meant to anyone else, to Paul it meant that he was a cripple. Like the kid in his class in the fourth grade, who was to be forever on crutches. Like the kid in the fifth grade who fell down on the floor in a fit and had a pencil thrust between his teeth so he would not bite his tongue off. Like the human toad who spent his day clutching the fire hydrant on Summit, drooling and vacant and making noises.

Like the beautiful young lady who was a poet, and whose left leg hurt constantly, who killed herself. Like the beautiful not quite as young lady who was becoming a hooker instead of an actress because—and only she knew it—the muscles in one upper arm were withered. Like the drunk young lady at lunch the other day who showed her hands to Paul and said, "I have deformed hands," and she did, and Paul thrust out both his arms and said, "I have a deformed arm," and the drunk young lady thought Paul was holding his shoulders that way for a joke, or to be kind, and there was no explaining. And Paul had his excuse that day for having another drink too many himself.

One day, Keith and Paul decided they had enough hair, enough balls, so that they needed jockstraps. It was not within their power to imagine that this was a subject to discuss with their mothers—both Keith and Paul got their allowances from the distaff side—and they weren't at all sure that their fathers would know, at their age, what a jockstrap was.

Keith's father had a great big leather drawstring-pouch of pennies way up on top of a bookcase, and with what was left of their allowances and this dividend from Mr. MacIlhenny, they were ready with the ready.

They walked to the village, and on Fifth Avenue was the sporting goods store. Keith and Paul walked resolutely past the hunting knives, the metal cylinders to keep matches dry, the Coleman lanterns, until they reached what would have to be the jockstrap department.

They gulped, and pitched their voices as low as they would go, and growled.

It turned out that jocks come in sizes, and when the clerk looked at them and said, "Small?" their voices returned to their natural timbre, they flushed and paid for the jocks and went home.

Well, not exactly. They went to Keith's house and in the relative privacy of his bedroom they took off their pants and put on the jockstraps.

The effect was miraculous and instantaneous. With all that soft down cuddled around their clydes, as one Keith and Paul got aching hard-ons.

It went on for some months, without the jockstraps.

Paul, now, has only recently stopped worrying about being homosexual, and he doesn't know the size of any article of clothing he wears.

One of the reasons Paul wanted to get into
the fifth grade was that then he could become a member of the Audubon Society. The way you got to be a
member was to build a birdhouse and enter it in the
Audubon competition—or the way you got to enter a
birdhouse was to join the society. He wasn't sure
which, but he sure as hell knew he wanted to build a
birdhouse.

He went and told his father about it, hoping against
hope that he would go down into the cellar with him
and help him build it. It was, as he had supposed, hope-
less. He already knew his father could not drive a car
or a nail, throw a ball or catch it. Hell, his father could
not even take the lid off a Mason jar once his mother
had screwed it shut.

His father did what he could. Told Jimmy the
chauffeur to help him.

They went down to the cellar together, and Jimmy,
never long on patience, built the whole birdhouse himself. Jimmy didn't believe the size hole the general instructions leaflet told, and he bored it big enough for an

owl to get in assways, and it was a wren house.

Paul knew he hadn't built the birdhouse, no matter what hearty con Jimmy gave him, and the day you were supposed to take the birdhouse to school with your name and grade on it, he felt like a thief.

On the way to school he thought about dumping it in a handy hedge, but he was a browbeaten and cowed young craven, and he didn't throw things away.

He became a member of the Audubon Society and put the birdhouse up on a tree in the back yard. It was painted and the roof was made of asphalt shingle and birds did not live in it; they crapped on it.

Paul remembers the way Jimmy drove each nail home, one tap to set it, two more to hammer it flush, holding the hammer by the end of the handle so the hammer head did the work.

When Paul grew up, a number of things followed from this. When his kids wanted to build something, Paul hovered, and when he found he was doing it instead of letting the kid do it, he walked away. He had also learned that when the job from which you make your living is judged arbitrarily and subjectively by other people, it preserves the sanity to do something with your hands. It doesn't matter a damn how nice or pretty or rich you are, a dovetail joint either fits or it doesn't. Nobody can tell you if it fits, if the wood doesn't tell you; nobody can say it doesn't fit, if the wood shows that it does.

The other thing he learned was that machines, if they are the right machines—typewriters or hammers or socket wrenches or toothpicks—do half the work for you. If they don't, they are lousy machines or you are not holding them right.

Mealtimes were a three-a-day nightmare for Paul. It had to do with his mother, the times in which she lived.

First, his mother had been poor as a child, then rich as wife and mother. She had been near enough to old-country traditions to believe that a fat child was not only a healthy child but a proof of prosperity, and when Paul was a kid, this was not far from a universal belief. A kid was supposed to be fat, have a bowel movement once a day, get good marks in school, speak when spoken to, and that was about it until you came of age.

So mealtime became a contest between Paul and his mother. He was very skinny, and to his mother, ever since the day he had been sent home by the school nurse as a possible malnutrition case, he had been an affront. By God, her kid was going to be as fat as any other kid, if it meant nailing his feet to the floor and force-feeding him through a funnel like a Strasbourg goose.

No matter how much he ate, it was not enough and as time wore on, after innumerable meals which ended in his gagging and saying, "I can't eat any more," he became more stubborn and determined not only not to eat more than he could but positively less.

When he had been very little, he had gone through a ritual that was quite common in those days. A mother across the table from a kid spooning mouthfuls of whatever accompanied by a refrain: "This spoon for Grandma, this one for the postman, a spoonful for the po-lice-man, one for Daddy . . . ," and in some cases the spooner would alternate mouthfuls with the spoonee, the spooner taking tiny bits of the mush in her mouth and smacking her lips and rolling her eyes.

Picnics, of which Paul's father was very fond, were a delight. Nobody paid any attention to what you ate; you could eat standing up or sitting down or walking around; and everything was arranged to be eaten from the hand. Delicatessen dinners were also great.

Every once in a while there would be a dinner of which Paul was particularly fond, and he would eat it all, and his mother did everything but give him a standing ovation.

But despite all this, and beef tea and beef juice and Maltine and eggnogs, he never was anything but skinny.

Until middle-age did what his mother could not. Potbelly and all, he kept in his head an image of himself as a waif, and slurped down chocolate floats, peanuts, coupes aux marrons and baked Alaskas,

French-fried potatoes and pasta, and despite the clear and present danger of having trouble cutting his own toenails and trousers mysteriously shrinking at the waistband, nothing would alter this impression.

Until a doctor looked at him and said, "First of all, you have to lose some weight," and put him on a diet, and now the poor bastard moons around, missing the postprandial applause, eats every bit of what the meager diet will allow, and searches wistfully for someone who will say, "We have to put a little flesh on those bones—how about a nice, stuffed baked potato with lots of butter?"

His body may be tubby, but his soul remains gaunt.

When he was a very little boy, Paul used to be dragooned from time to time and impressed into a shopping gang. His mother and his two sisters were, it seemed to Paul, always shopping. Always for not just one thing, but for an outfit. As soon as Christmas was over, they were on the trail of spring outfits; the middle of the summer it was time to track down what they were going to wear in the fall.

This meant going to the department stores in New York, ordering one of each from every store, trying them on at home, sending them all back, or keeping one and wishing they had kept the other.

The first time Paul was taken along, all he could remember was endless hours standing in elevators with ladies' butts up against his nose, being stepped on, and being tugged and pulled and arranged into clothes that mostly itched.

Finally, there was, in this first expedition, a suit that didn't itch. It was a white sailor suit; the pants did not button on the blouse because they were inside the blouse, and around the middy neck was slung, on a braid of course, an entirely beautiful wooden whistle.

He liked that suit, and his mother said, "You don't really like it, you just want that whistle." And he squirmed while the salesman laughed, and he didn't get that suit.

Over the years, at one time or another, Paul has purchased (and not been able to play) a slide whistle, a number of harmonicas, a descant recorder, a tenor recorder, a cornet, a flute, and a baroque bassoon.

Keith had a pair of hunting boots that were laced with rawhide strips and came to his knees, and had a small pocket with a snap-over flap, in which was stored a jackknife. The jackknife came with the boots, and the boots were on sale at the Army-Navy store. Paul went in and found out the price. It was not even close to the maximum he felt able to save from his allowance; anyhow, these were shoes and his mother was supposed to buy his shoes. He still was not old enough to keep his mouth shut, and in three embarrassing minutes his mother said, "You only want the boots for the knife." And he got neither. He stole his first knife about a week from then, from a chalk box in the cloakroom at school.

Paul in his adulthood has bought a knife in every city he has ever gone to. Friends of his are implored to bring back, from whatever foreign country they go to, a knife of the country, and when Paul sees a friend with a knife, that friend is made miserable until he gives Paul that knife.

It never works out. Like all of us, Paul doesn't want that baroque bassoon—he wants that wooden whistle, and none of the knives is anything like the one that Keith carried in his hunting boot.

It happened to Paul shortly after he had discovered the public library. And when that was, he couldn't be sure, any more than he could really remember when he had learned to read. One day he couldn't read, and the next day he could, and one day he didn't have a public library card, and the next day he did.

He could never remember what book it was either, but all of a sudden there it was in his hand, and something clicked in his head and he realized that the book had not always existed, that somewhere, sometime, it had been just an idea in the author's head, and then he had set it down and somebody decided to set each word in print and put all the pages together in a binding and the public library had bought it and put it on a shelf and he, Paul, had taken it out, and now he was reading it and it was magic. Somebody any number of years ago, whom Paul had never met, was talking to Paul, and nobody else.

He went around in a daze the rest of the afternoon.

He went around in a daze the rest of his life. If somebody else could do it, he could, too. And did. And the other night he heard somebody quote an unknown author who said, "Oh, but you should have seen it before I wrote it."

In the days when Paul was a little kid and they lived in the suburbs, the organization of society on the block was different from what it is now.

It was vertical. Kids passed freely from one level to another, and had considerable contact with other kids and adults not of their age. By the time Paul was grown and was a father and lived with his kids in the suburbs, it had become a horizontal society. Five-year-olds played with five-year-olds, first year of high school associated almost exclusively with their peers. Part of the change had to do with the greater mobility of everyone, including kids. In Paul's childhood, the horizon loomed at either end of the block he lived on, and in the other direction the ancient map legend would have suited the land a block away on either side: "Here be monsters."

This meant that anyone on the block was familiar, in the real sense of that word. Anybody's older sister was your older sister, Keith's Uncle Charlie was your Uncle

Charlie, and Mrs. MacIlhenny would put a bandage on your skinned knee if your mother was not at home.

Nowadays the children are schlepped miles to play with another kid exactly like themselves. On Paul's block, you went to someone's house on the block, and if who you were looking for was not there, you stayed and talked to whoever was there.

You learned a lot that way. You learned that given half a chance Manny's second cousin would put his hand on your thigh, you learned that the reason Mrs. Kaplan hadn't been out of the house in days was her hair dye (heavens!) had gone wrong, and her poll was iridescent and multicolored like a blackbird's wing, that Dr. Telfer was usually stoned by one o'clock and would give you tongue depressors to make model airplane wings with, that Charlie Vinton's older brother smeared chocolate on his cock and let their Newfoundland dog lick it off.

A never-ending source of delight was Manny's mother. In the first place she was so short that when she rode on the trolley car her feet dangled. She was very Russian and very excitable, and it was at her house that Paul went, for the first and last time, to a tea-towel party. You sat in their baronially furnished dining room with the genuine monk's cope spreadeagled on the wall, and there was a samovar on the table, and from it gushed a fountain of very hot, very strong tea. It was served in glasses, with raspberry jam swirling at the bottom, and the glass was too hot to touch. You drank tea and argued (Paul was adolescent then) about Zionism, and Chekhov, and Chaliapin, and you drank endless glasses of the fragrant tea. And you got excited and shouted, and sweated. Over the high back of each chair was a tea towel, fine linen embroidered with Russian cross-stitch, and when the sweat was running off your face into the tea and your hands were so wet that the glass almost slipped through your hand, you whipped one arm up over your head and back, grabbed the tea towel, and mopped. Then you got up and hung the towel over the high back of your chair again, so it could dry out for the next round.

You went home sloshing and emotionally purged.

But Manny's mother's finest hour was when they bought a Russian wolfhound. At three o'clock every afternoon—she wanted it out of the way before the kids came home from school—the borzoi attached Mrs. Cavery to the loose end of its leash and took her for a run. She would come tearing down the street, her feet hardly touching the ground, and saying curious things in Russian while the dog slavered and stretched its legs. You could see only Mrs. Cavery's head bobbing above the hedge, and you sat there hugging yourself with delight until the full splendor of the scene was before your eyes. Which strained with tears.

Mrs. Cavery died the other day. It was the first time he had thought of her in years. Possibly she was a magnificent human being, full of frailty and desire, good sense, and enormous emotional depth, a real human being. But all Paul could think of was the way she came pelting down the street, gasping and shouting, and all Paul did when he heard she had died was to laugh and laugh.

That certain people, of little significance at the time, should loom up later in Paul's memory as creatures of great significance was not surprising.

Ruth Jarvey wore her fountain pen on a ribbon around her neck, and it nestled warmly between her new breasts, and that was something to remember. Dr. Llewellyn, who operated on all the mastoiditis cases in town, used to, it was said, totter around all week with an agonizing hang-over and palsied hands, and come into the operating room drunk and steady as a rock.

But why, for all time in Paul's rag bag of a head, should there be a memory of a little brass cup that stood in the center of the planchette of the ouija (pronounced weejee) board? There was nothing so special about it, and the ouija board was a dud, but the cup remains, sunk in Paul's cortex.

And, cups again, the two little metal receptacles on the phonograph, one a hemisphere for new needles, and the other with a top, concentric hole in the center for used needles when the new ones gave out, at which point one emptied the used needles into the new-needles cup, and all was *aria da capo*.

The leather coat that his father brought back from Europe, an aviator's from the First World War.

The copper nugget in the museum jar shining through some somewhat viscous liquid.

The stuffed owl, that was a delight to touch.

The deer head, which was not.

His father's truss, of leather and chamois and metal, a spare cock which he put on and off, a symbol of what Paul had waiting for him when he grew up.

First his grandfather died. Then Mr. Morris walked into the ocean up to his neck and just kept on going. Then Manny's father was shouting and his whole face turned black and he fell down dead. Then Keith's mother had a baby and the baby lived but she didn't, and Mr. MacIlhenny got a new Mrs. MacIlhenny. Then Michael's father dove into the lake and hit his head on a stone and didn't come up again.

And one night Paul went to sleep, and when he woke up in the morning his father was dead.

He had known all along that his father was going to die, but he didn't know when, and this happened on a very bad night. He, for some reason no one ever was able to explain to him in later years, had been moved out of his own room into the room next to his mother and father's bedroom, and the night his father was dying he kept shouting and begging for the needle. Paul knew by this time that the needle was a hypodermic needle, and it was something used *in extremis* (as in those days an X ray was) and he knew that Doctor Novotny would be by pretty soon and give his father the needle and he would not have to hear the shouting and the crying. Dr. Novotny lived down the street and around each eye was permanently what looked to Paul like a black bruise, and Paul's father liked Dr. Novotny, and his mother did not, and Paul was frightened of his hawklike face with the two black patches.

Paul also knew that the reason his father liked Dr. Novotny was because he gave him the needle, and that was the same reason his mother had for not liking him.

But at the moment all Paul knew was that he was out of his own room, his own bed, because of his father, and hearing the crying and the pleading and the shouting. And lying there Paul said, "God damn you, shut *up!*"

And in the morning his father was dead.

The next few weeks were very strange. His sisters came home, but, it turned out, he, Paul, was the important child. He was so near his bar mitzvah that he was qualified as an adult, and Manny's older brother, The Bull, came by and taught him, very gently and patiently, to say kaddish.

People brought food, and there was company—friends and relatives—all day long.

Just as with the broken leg and arm, he was an object of great interest, and just as quickly as it had with his arm and leg, the interest in him as the bereaved stopped.

He was, then, twice a cripple and as with all cripples

was read out of the pack. He and Mike and Manny and Keith became a pack of their own.

But before that there was the funeral, and the coffin standing in the center of the living room, and before it was closed the people who wanted to look at the corpse were to step forward. Helen did not, Pearl did not, his mother did not; and then Paul started toward it (full of terror and curiosity), and his mother took him by the arm and held him back and whispered to him, "Don't."

It took Paul many, many years to absorb the fact that his father was dead, and once, a little loaded, he saw the movie *The Life of Emile Zola* and Joseph Schildkraut as Dreyfus looked so exactly like his father, with the same first name and second name beginning with the same initial, that in his muzzy mind a perfectly detailed plan was forming, to go to Hollywood and announce himself to his masquerading father.

For a long time he would not go to funerals, and then from time to time he went, and always looked at the body in the coffin, each time overcome by the difference between a live body and a dead one.

And although many, many years have gone by since his father's death, Paul is always startled, on meeting anyone over the age of twenty, to discover he has a complete set of living parents.

The day his father died was the end of Paul's childhood. No child is aware of his own mortality; there are his mother and father, ages older than he, and they are not dead, although in a child's eyes they have already lived next to forever.

If they don't die, he is not going to die.

And then his father died.

If your father dies, you can die, too.

So his father died. Paul's adulthood was still a long way off.

And his childhood was over.

Format by Vivian Ostrow
Set in 11/14 Caledonia
Composed, printed and bound by The Haddon Craftsmen, Inc.
HARPER & ROW, PUBLISHERS, INCORPORATED